KS3 Maths

Essential SATS Practice

It's another Quality Book from CGP

It's packed with lots of nasty questions — because they're
the sort you'll get in the exam.

Practise getting these questions right and you'll
sweat a lot less on the big day.

Contents

Published by Coordination Group Publications Ltd.

Contributors:

Andrew Ballard, Alison Chisholm, Jane Chow, Sally Gill, Christine Griffiths, Sharon Keeley,
Mark Moody, Mark Turner, Julie Wakeling, Janet West, Jeanette Whiteman.

With thanks to Vicky Daniel for the proofreading.

Jolly bits of clipart from CorelDRAW

Printed by Elanders Hindson, Newcastle upon Tyne

ISBN: 1 84146 127 X

Groovy website: www.cgpbooks.co.uk

Section One — Numbers Mostly

Big Numbers

1 Peter has carried out a survey of the number of people at his university.

(a) There are three hundred and nineteen lecturers at the university.
Write this number in figures.

....

(b) 20 605 students attend the university.
Write the number 20 605 in words.

....

(c) 15 843 students live in halls of residence.
In the number 15 843, the figure 4 has the value of 40. What is the value of the figure 5?

....

2 Nick has six number cards.

$$1 \quad 8 \quad 7 \quad 3 \quad 6 \quad 2$$

Nick is asked to arrange the cards to make different numbers.

(a) Write down the largest number Nick can make.

....

(b) What is the smallest five-digit number Nick can make?

....

(c) What is the closest number to 260 that Nick can make?

....

(d) Write down in words the smallest four-digit number Nick can make.

....

Plus, Minus, Times & Divide

1 Look at the calculations in the table below.
Tick (✓) ones that are correct, cross (✗) ones that are wrong.

Calculation	✓ or ✗
2 + 5 = 5 + 2	✓
7 − 2 = 2 − 7	✗
8 × 4 = 4 × 8	✓
9 ÷ 3 = 3 ÷ 9	✗

2 Work out:

(a) 253 + 475 = ... *728* ....

(b) 1026 − 859 = ... *167* ....

(c) 49 × 8 = ... *302* ....

33

(d) 132 ÷ 4 = ...

3 Solve these problems.

(a) What number should you add to 89 to make 160? .... *71* ....

(b) What number should you multiply 15 by to make 1860? .... *124* ....

(c) Add 456 to half of 1068. .... *990* ....

(d) How much less than 1000 is 26 × 38? .... *12* ....

....

4 Use the symbols +, −, × or ÷ to make each of the following calculations correct.

Example: 9 − 3 = 12 ÷ 2

(a) 10 ...+... 6 = 4 ...×... 4   (c) 10 ...×... 2 = 64 ...÷... 8

(b) 45 ...÷... 9 = 2 ...+... 3   (d) 5 ...×... 5 = 12 ...−... 12

Patterns with Times & Divide

1   Look at the sum in the box.

$$6 \times 16 = 96$$

Use this sum to help you work out:

(a) $96 \div 16 =$ .... 6 ....

(b) $12 \times 16 =$ .... 192 ....

(c) $96 \div 32 =$ .... 3 ....

(d) $192 \div 16 =$ .... 12 ....

2   There are 25 chocolate biscuits in a packet. One packet of biscuits costs £1.25.

(a)   How many biscuits are there in 7 packets?

.... 175 ....

(b)   How much do 7 packets of biscuits cost?

.... £8.75 ....

(c)   How much do fifty biscuits cost?

.... £62.50 ....

(d)   How many packets of biscuits could you buy for £5?

.... 4 ....

3   Four identical pots of yoghurt weigh 500 grams.

(a)   How much do two pots of yoghurt weigh? .... 1Kg ....

(b)   How much do twelve pots of yoghurt weigh? .... 60Kg ....

(c)   A box of yoghurts weighs 2500 g.
      How many pots of yoghurt are in the box? .... 5 ....

Multiplying by 10, 100, 1000 etc.

1 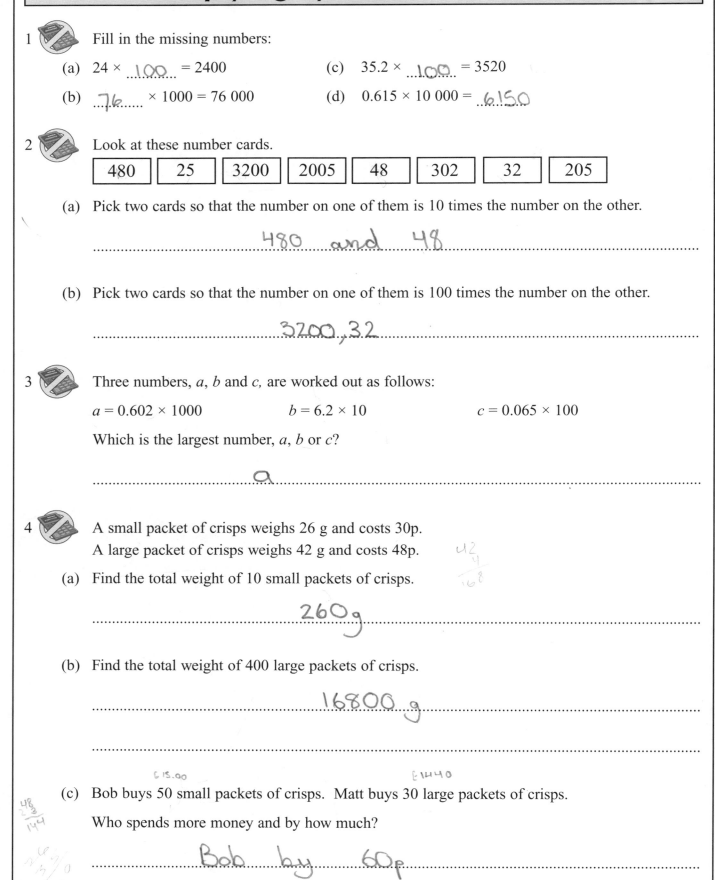 Fill in the missing numbers:

(a) 24 × ...100... = 2400

(c) 35.2 × ...100... = 3520

(b) ...76... × 1000 = 76 000

(d) 0.615 × 10 000 = ...6150...

2 Look at these number cards.

| 480 | 25 | 3200 | 2005 | 48 | 302 | 32 | 205 |

(a) Pick two cards so that the number on one of them is 10 times the number on the other.

480 and 48

(b) Pick two cards so that the number on one of them is 100 times the number on the other.

3200, 32

3 Three numbers, *a*, *b* and *c,* are worked out as follows:

$a = 0.602 \times 1000$ $b = 6.2 \times 10$ $c = 0.065 \times 100$

Which is the largest number, *a*, *b* or *c*?

a

4 A small packet of crisps weighs 26 g and costs 30p.
A large packet of crisps weighs 42 g and costs 48p.

42
4
168

(a) Find the total weight of 10 small packets of crisps.

260 g

(b) Find the total weight of 400 large packets of crisps.

16800 g

£15.00   £1440

(c) Bob buys 50 small packets of crisps. Matt buys 30 large packets of crisps.

Who spends more money and by how much?

Bob by 60p

48
2
144

6
3 0
3

Dividing by 10, 100, 1000 etc.

1 Fill in the missing numbers:

(a) $500 \div 10 =$ _50_

(b) $3400 \div$ _100_ $= 34$

(c) _82000_ $\div 1000 = 82$

(d) $25 \div 10 =$ _2.5_

(e) $70 \div 200 =$ _0.35_

(f) $6400 \div$ _1000_ $= 6.4$

(g) $7.5 \div 10 =$ _0.75_

(h) $4500 \div 10\,000 =$ _0.45_

2 18 700 people attended a football match.

(a) 1 person in 10 bought a match programme.
How many programmes were sold?

.... _1870_ ....

(b) 1 person in 100 bought a hamburger.
How many hamburgers were sold?

.... _187_ ....

3 A school bought 80 Maths books at a total cost of £1200.

(a) How much does one book cost?

.... _£15_ ....

A book is made up of a front and back cover and 300 pages.
The front and back covers are 1 mm thick each.
The total thickness of the book is 38 mm.

(b) Work out the thickness of one page of the book.

.... _0.12 mm_ ....

Multiples & Factors

1 Answer the following questions about multiples and factors.

(a) (i) List all the multiples of 2 between 1 and 20. 4,6,8,10,12,14,16,18,20

(ii) List all the multiples of 5 between 1 and 20. 5,10,15,20

(iii) List the multiples of both 2 **and** 5 between 1 and 20.

10,20

(b) Find all the factors of:

(i) 12 1,2,6,3,4,12

(ii) 20 20,1,10,2,5,4,2

(iii) 36 36,1,6,3,12,2,18,4

(iv) Which numbers are factors of 12, 20 **and** 36?

1,2,4

2 Here is a set of winning Lotto numbers.

(2) (10) (16) (24) (5) (40)

(a) Which Lotto numbers are multiples of 2? 2,10,16,24,40

(b) Which Lotto numbers are multiples of both 4 and 8? 16,24,40

(c) Which Lotto numbers are factors of 20? 10,2,5

(d) Which Lotto numbers are not factors of 120? 16

(e) Which Lotto number is a multiple of 12 and a factor of 48?

24

Odd, Even, Square & Cube Numbers

1   Gemma has six coins in her purse:

1p   2p   5p   10p   20p   50p

(a) She buys sweets using all her even valued coins. She does not get any change. How much do the sweets cost?

.... 82p ....

(b) How much money does she have left in her purse?

.... 6p ....

2   Find the value of:

83 65 427

(a) 18^2 .... 324 ....

(b) 25^3 .... 625 ....

(c) Forty-two squared .... 1764 ....

(d) Two hundred and three cubed ....

3   Look at this list of numbers:

1   4   8   16   25   27   38   49   55   64

(a) Write down all the even numbers. 4,8,16,38,64 ....

(b) Write down all the odd square numbers. 1,25,27,49,55 ....

(c) Write down all the odd cube numbers. 8,18,64 ....

(d) Which numbers are both square and cube numbers? 49 ....

Prime Numbers

1. Write down:

   (a) an even prime number. _____ 2 _____

   (b) the first six prime numbers. _____ 2,3,5,7,11,13 _____

   (c) all the prime numbers between 25 and 35.

   29,31,

2. Show that:

   (a) 89 is a prime number.

   _____ Factors of 89: 1,89 _____

   (b) 91 is not a prime number.

   _____ Factors of 91: 1,91,13,7 _____

3. Here are 10 numbered counters.

   (1) (2) (5) (9) (11) (17) (21) (23) (37) (42)

   (a) Which counters are less than 30 and are prime numbers?

   _____ 2,5,11,17,23 _____

   (b) Which counters are prime numbers and factors of 20?

   _____ 2,5 _____

   (c) Is 37 a prime number? Show your working.

   No, Factor of 37: 1,37

   (d) What is the sum of the non-prime numbered counters?

   73

Ratio

1   Four computers cost £5450.

(a) How much do ten computers cost?

.... £9000 ....

(b) In an office, the ratio of printers to computers is 2:9.
     If there are 45 computers in the office, how many printers are there?

.... 7 ....

2   Kate and Deborah share £3600 in the ratio 4:5.

(a) How much more money than Kate does Deborah receive?

.... £1600,£700 ....

Sam is 6 years old. Ed is three years older than Sam.
Sam and Ed share a bag of 45 sweets in the ratio of their ages.

(b) How many sweets does Ed get?

.... 20 ....

3   Here is a recipe for chocolate chip buns:

Chocolate Chip Buns (*makes 16*)
170 g flour   2 eggs
100 g butter   50 g chocolate chips
140 g sugar   3 tablespoons milk

(a) A food technology teacher is making 48 buns.

(i)   How much butter does she need? .... 300g ....

(ii) How flour does she need? .... 70g ....

(b) The teacher only has 5 eggs. How many buns can she make?

.... 32 ....

Money

1 ABC Theatre Group is putting on a production of "Sleeping Beauty".

> *ABC Theatre Group presents:*
> ## *Sleeping Beauty*
> **Ticket Prices**
> | | |
> |---|---|
> | Adult | £9.50 |
> | Child (under 16) | £6.25 |
> | Family ticket (2 adults & 2 children) | £28 |

(a) How much do 5 child tickets cost? ....£31.25..

(b) Judy bought 4 adult tickets and 1 child ticket.
How much change did she receive from a £50 note?

.............................£5.75...

(c) How much cheaper is it to buy a family ticket compared to buying two adult and two child tickets separately? Show your working.

.............................£31.49...

....

2 Michael is out Christmas shopping.

(a) Five Christmas trees cost £79.
How much does one tree cost?

$$5\overline{\smash{)}79.00}\ \ ^{15.80}$$

.............................£15.80...

(b) Six packs of Christmas cards cost £16.20.
Michael bought two packs of Christmas cards and 30 postage stamps for £11.70.

(i) Find the price of one pack of Christmas cards.

.............................£2.70...

(ii) Find the price of a postage stamp. Show your working.

.............................£7.00...

....

Multiplication without a Calculator

1 Here is the 32 times table:

$1 \times 32 = 32$
$2 \times 32 = 64$
$3 \times 32 = 96$
$4 \times 32 = 128$
$5 \times 32 = 160$
$6 \times 32 = 192$
$7 \times 32 = 224$
$8 \times 32 = 256$
$9 \times 32 = 288$
$10 \times 32 = 320$

(a) Fill in the missing numbers in the table.

(b) Use the 32 times table to help you complete the sums below.

(i) $32 \times 5 =$ 160

(ii) $12 \times 32 =$ 384

(iii) $20 \times 32 =$ 640

(iv) $18 \times 32 =$ 576

2 A coach ticket from Manchester to London costs £19.50.
A train ticket from Manchester to London costs £25.

How much more would it cost for 6 people to travel by train from Manchester to London rather than by coach? Show your working.

....

....

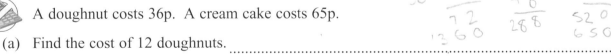

3 A doughnut costs 36p. A cream cake costs 65p.

(a) Find the cost of 12 doughnuts. ....

.... £4.32

(b) Find the cost of 28 cream cakes. .... £10.35 ....

....

(c) Jenny buys 8 doughnuts and 18 cream cakes.
How much change does she receive from £20? Show your working.

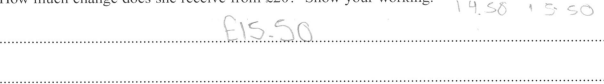

.... £15.50 ....

....

Division without a Calculator

1   A box can hold a maximum of 6 eggs.

   (a)   How many boxes are needed for 336 eggs?

   ....

   (b)   How many boxes are needed for 608 eggs?

   ....

   (c)   56 chickens lay 9 eggs each.
         How many boxes are needed to pack these eggs?

   ....

   ....

2   The table shows the amount of money three boys save each week.

	Money saved per week
Andy	£5
Lewis	£8
Rick	£4

£128   £100   £63

   (a)   How many weeks does Lewis have to save for in order to buy the MP3 player?

   ....

   (b)   Andy wants the skateboard.
         How many weeks does he have to save for before he can buy it?

   ....

   (c)   Rick wants to buy a mobile phone. He has already saved up £40.
         How many more weeks does he have to save for?

   ....

Using Formulas

1 Look at these calculations.

Tick (✓) ones that are correct. Cross (✗) ones that are wrong.

Calculation	✓ or ✗
$(10 + 2) - 4 = 10 + 2 - 4$	✓
$10 + (2 \times 4) = 10 + 2 \times 4$	✓
$10 \times (4 + 2) = 10 \times 4 + 2$	✗
$(10 - 4) \div 2 = 10 - 4 \div 2$	✗
$(10 \div 2) \times 4 - 2 = 10 \div 2 \times 4 - 2$	✓

2 If $a = -2$, $b = 5$ and $c = 8$, work out:

(a) a^2b ....

(b) $2a + bc$ ....

(c) $a(b + c)$ ....

(d) $2b^2 + c^2 - a^2$ ....

3 To convert temperatures from degrees Fahrenheit (°F) to Celsius (°C), we use the formula:

$$C = \frac{5(F - 32)}{9}$$

where C is the temperature in °C and F is the temperature in °F.

(a) Convert 32 °F to °C.

....

(b) Convert 212 °F to °C.

....

(c) Convert 68 °F to °C.

....

Ordering Decimals

1 Put each set of numbers in order of size, starting with the smallest.

   (a)   4.8   5.72   3.09   4.79   5.17   3.5

....

   (b)   0.4   0.303   0.43   0.31   0.44   0.043

....

2 The table shows the heights and weights of five children.

Name of child	Height (metres)	Weight (kilograms)
Emily	0.88	18.06
Georgina	0.858	18.5
Thomas	0.904	20.3
Imogen	0.942	20.09
Elliot	0.82	18.1

   (a) Which child is the tallest?

....

   (b) Which child is the lightest?

....

   (c) Write down the names of the children in height order starting with the shortest child.

....

   (d) Write down the names of the children in weight order starting with the heaviest child.

....

Numbers Mostly Mini-Exam (1)

1 Matthias won £1 403 720 on the football pools.

(a) Write down the amount of money Matthias won in words.

....

....

(b) Matthias gave twenty thousand, three hundred and five pounds to the local charity.

Write down this amount in figures. ....

(c) Tariq won seven thousand, five hundred and thirty four pounds more than Matthias on the Lotto. Write down the amount in figures that Tariq won.

....

2 Sabrina and Chris are thinking of ways of getting from one number to another.

(a) Chris thinks of three different ways of getting from 5 to 20: $5 \rightarrow 20$

Fill in the gaps below to show how Chris can get from 5 to 20.

(i) add ....

(ii) multiply by ....

(iii) multiply by 2, then either add .... or multiply by ....

(b) Sabrina finds a way of changing 20 to 5. Her method also changes 32 to 8.

$20 \rightarrow 5 \qquad 32 \rightarrow 8$

What **one** thing could Sabrina do to get from 20 to 5 **and** from 32 to 8?

....

3 Here are six number cards.

$\boxed{3} \quad \boxed{3} \quad \boxed{3} \quad \boxed{8} \quad \boxed{8} \quad \boxed{8}$

Use five of the cards to make this sum correct:

$$
\begin{array}{r}
\square\,\square\,\square \\
+\ \ \square\,\square \\
\hline
4\ \ 2\ \ 6
\end{array}
$$

Numbers Mostly Mini-Exam (1)

4 3 litres of orange juice costs £1.56.

   (a) Find the cost of 7 litres of orange juice. ....

   (b) How many litres of orange juice can I buy for £15.60? ....

5 Write these amounts of money in order of size starting with the smallest amount.

£0.34 £0.07 £0.70 £0.43 £0.47 £3.04 £7.00

....

6   Look at these four numbers: 2   4   7   9

Here is a diagram for sorting numbers:

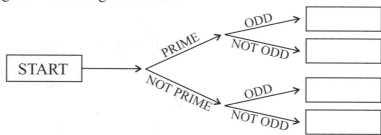

   (a) Write the four numbers in the correct boxes in the diagram.

   (b) Which of the four numbers is a multiple of 3? ....

   (c) Which of the four numbers are factors of 18? ....

   (d) Of the four numbers, which ones are square numbers? ....

7 Look at this multiplication table.

×	14	15	16	17	18
31	434	465	496	527	558
32	448	480	512	544	576
33	462	495	528	561	594
34	476	510	544	578	612
35	490	525	560	595	630

Use the table to complete the sums below.

(a) $32 \times 17 =$ ....

(b) $18 \times$ .... $= 612$

(c) $528 \div 16 =$ ....

(d) .... $\times$ .... $= 476$

Numbers Mostly Mini-Exam (2)

1   There are 345 Year 9 pupils at a secondary school.

   (a)   The ratio of girls to boys is 7:8.
         How many girls are there? Show your working.

         ....

   (b)   In Year 10, the ratio of girls to boys is 5:6. There are 125 girls.
         How many boys are there? Show your working.

         ....

2   A chocolate bar from a machine costs 45p.
     The table shows the coins that were put into the machine in one day.

Coin	Number of coins
50p	32
20p	15
10p	42
5p	49

     How many chocolate bars were sold that day?

     ....

     ....

3   A supermarket sells bottles of milk in three different sizes.

     | 568 ml bottles at 37p |
     | 2 litre bottles at 99p |
     | 3.25 litre bottles at £1.59 |

     Which bottle of milk represents the best value for money? Show your working.

     ....

     ....

Numbers Mostly Mini-Exam (2)

4   Physicists use equations to work out physical quantities.

(a)   A well-known equation by Isaac Newton is $F = ma$.
Find the value of F when $m = 45$ and $a = 7.8$. Show your working.

....

(b)   An equation to find the speed of a car is $v = u + at$.
Find the value of v when $u = 10.5$, $a = 6.8$ and $t = 12$. Show your working.

....

5   Here are four number cards.

| 4 | | 7 | | 2 | | 3 |

(a)   Choose two of the number cards to make a prime number less than 35.

....

(b)   Choose two of the number cards to make a prime number greater than 50.
Show that the number you have chosen is prime.

....

6   Dr Williamson is buying some stationery for his surgery.

(a)   5 notebooks cost £10.80.
Find the cost of 3 notebooks.

....

....

(b)   15 pens cost £11.25.
Find the cost of 34 pens.

....

....

Perimeter

1 The diagram below shows a piece of paper.

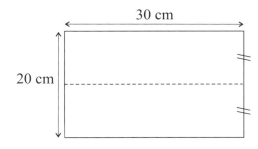

30 cm

20 cm

(a) What is the perimeter of the sheet of paper?

....

....

(b) If I cut along the dotted line, what is the perimeter of one of the smaller rectangles?

....

2 Find the perimeter of this triangle.
Measure in cm and give your answer to one decimal place.

....

....

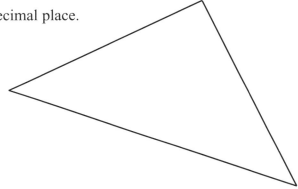

3 Use the axes given below for this question.

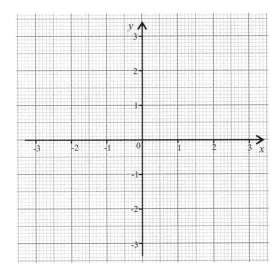

(a) Plot these coordinates and join the points in order to make a pentagon.
(2, 0)   (0, –2)   (–2, –2)   (–2, 2)   (2, 3)

(b) What is the perimeter of the pentagon?
Give your answer in mm.

....

....

Area

1   Find the area of this rectangle.
State the units in your answer.

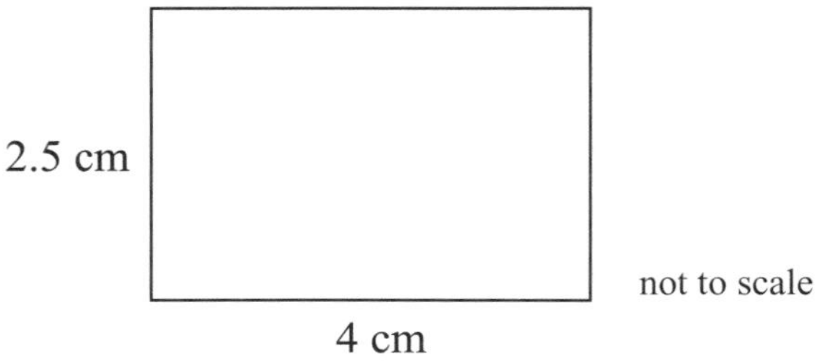

....

....

2.5 cm

4 cm

not to scale

2   The diagram below shows a right-angled triangle.

3 cm   not to scale

4 cm

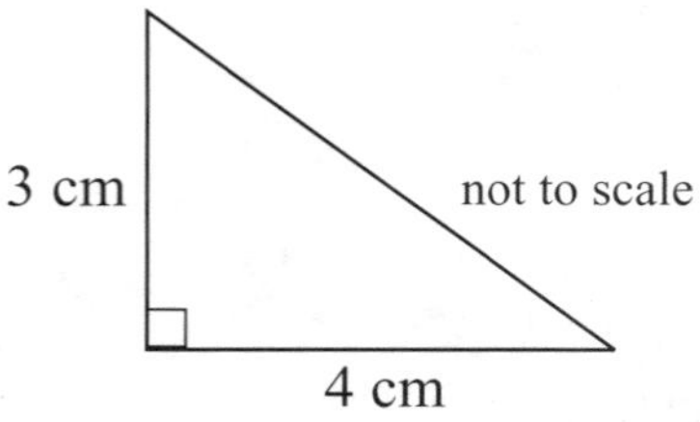

(a)   Explain how to find the area of a right-angled triangle.

....

....

....

(b)   What is the area of this triangle?

....

3   Look at the diagram of a flower bed shown below:

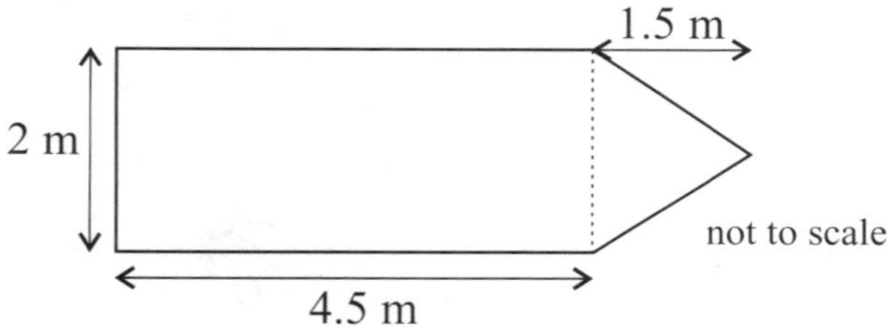

1.5 m

2 m

4.5 m

not to scale

What is the area of the flower bed? Show all your working.

....

....

4   The length of a rectangle is 6 cm and the area is 21 cm².
What is the width of this rectangle?

....

Area

1 Find the area of this triangle.

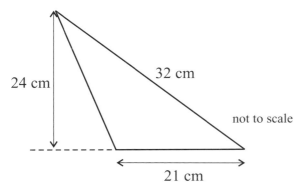

24 cm

32 cm

not to scale

21 cm

....

....

2 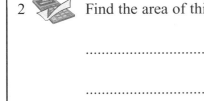 Find the area of this T shape.

....

....

....

....

20 cm

3 cm

7 cm

7 cm

16 cm

not to
scale

3 Which shape has the larger area — the rectangle or the rhombus?
Show your method clearly.

....

....

....

....

not to scale

4.5 cm

9.2 cm

8 cm

3 cm   3 cm

8 cm

....

....

....

Circles

1 Look at the picture of a plate shown below:

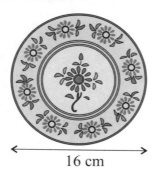

16 cm

(a) Circle the best estimate for the circumference of this plate?

25 cm   50 cm   200 cm

(b) Give a reason for your answer.

....

....

(handwritten working: πr² ; 2164.00 / 3.45 ; 32000 ; 256000 ; 192000 ; 2080.00)

2  This bicycle wheel has a diameter of 21 inches.

What is its circumference? Give your answer to the nearest inch.

....

....

21 inches

3 What is the area of the circle on the right?

....

....

....

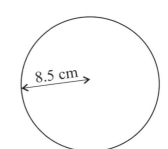

8.5 cm

Circles

1 Fill in the gaps in the table below:

radius	diameter	circumference	area
5 cm			
		82.7 cm	

2 This diagram shows the outline of a running track.
The track has two straight sections and semi-circular ends.

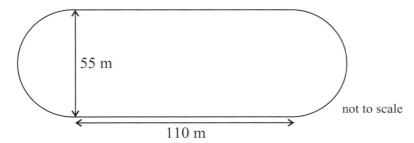

55 m

110 m

not to scale

(a) What is the distance around the outside edge of this running track?

....

Jayne runs at an average speed of 3.5 m/s.

The formula relating speed, distance and time is: $\text{time} = \dfrac{\text{distance}}{\text{speed}}$.

(b) How many minutes would it take Jayne to run around this track?
Give your answer to 1 decimal place.

....

....

3 Mike has two circular discs. One is red with a diameter of 18.2 cm.
The other is yellow with an area of 280 cm².
Which disc is larger? Show your method clearly.

....

....

....

Solids & Nets

1 Look at the diagrams. Tick the boxes below the two nets which will fold up to make cubes.

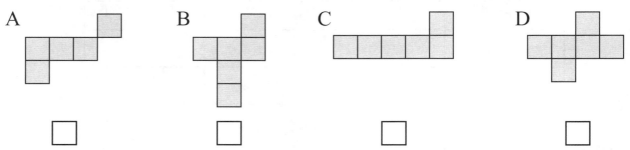

A   B   C   D

☐   ☐   ☐   ☐

2 Below are two solids and two nets.

  (a) Draw lines to connect each solid to its correct net.

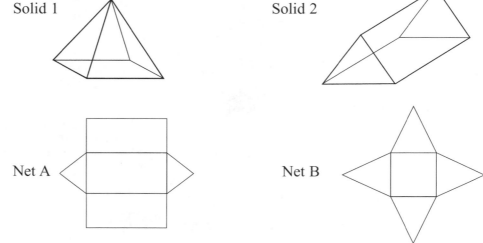

Solid 1   Solid 2

Net A   Net B

  (b) Write down the name of:

Solid 1 ....

Solid 2 ....

3 This is a net of a cuboid.

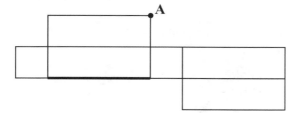

A

  (a) Draw another ● to show which part of the net will meet corner A when the net is folded into a cuboid.

  (b) Draw a bold line to show which edge will meet the bold line marked.

Volume & Capacity

1 A cube is a regular solid.

  (a) Sketch a cube in the space below, including its hidden lines.

  (b) What is the volume of a cube with sides 4 cm long?

  ....

2 What is the volume of each of these cuboids?

  (a)

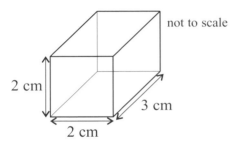

  2 cm

  2 cm   3 cm

  not to scale

  (b)

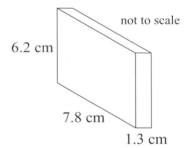

  6.2 cm

  7.8 cm

  1.3 cm

  not to scale

  ....

3 A child has a wooden box filled with wooden bricks.
  The wooden box is in the shape of a cube with sides 20 cm long.
  The small coloured bricks are all cubes with sides 4 cm long.

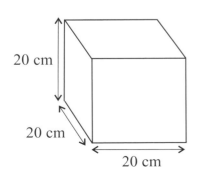

20 cm

20 cm

20 cm

not to scale

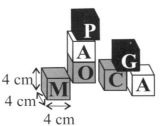

4 cm

4 cm

4 cm

How many small bricks fit in the large box?

....

....

....

Symmetry

1 Complete the table below:

	Number of lines of symmetry	Order of rotational symmetry
rectangle	2	
parallelogram		2
kite		1

2 Reflect these shapes in the mirror lines. You may use a mirror or tracing paper to help you.

(a)

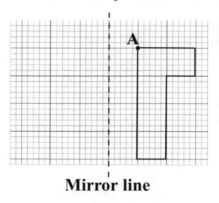

Mirror line

(b)

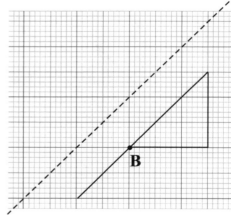

Mirror line

3 Draw a plane of symmetry on this pentagonal prism.

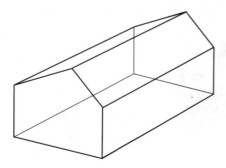

Symmetry & Tessellations

1. Which of the letters below has:

ROSE

   (a) 2 lines of symmetry? ....

   (b) rotational symmetry of order 2? ....

   (c) 1 line of symmetry? ....

2. Draw a tessellating pattern using at least six more of the shapes below.

3. This diagram shows a tiled floor.

   (a) Name the 2 shapes being used:

   .... and ....

   (b) Write down three properties of a regular **hexagon**:

   1. ....

   2. ....

   3. ....

2D & 3D Shapes

1 Draw lines to join each shape with its correct label.

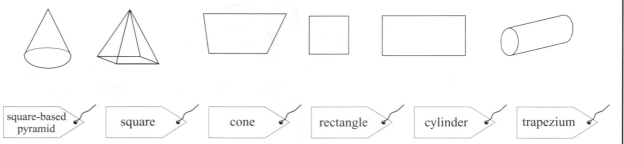

| square-based pyramid | square | cone | rectangle | cylinder | trapezium |

2 A parallelogram and a rhombus are both four sided shapes.

(a) Write down one other thing that is the same about a parallelogram and a rhombus.

....

(b) Write down one thing that is different about a parallelogram and a rhombus.

....

3 Complete this table about triangles:

Type of Triangle	Right-angled triangle		
Diagram			
One Property			all sides are different lengths and all angles are different

4 A square-based pyramid is glued to fit exactly on top of a cuboid.

(a) How many vertices does the square based pyramid have? ....

(b) How many vertices does the cuboid have? ....

(c) How many vertices will the new solid have?

....

Regular Polygons

1   This shape is a regular pentagon.

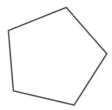

(a) Draw all the lines of symmetry on the pentagon.
You may use a mirror or tracing paper to help you.

(b) What is the order of rotational symmetry of a regular pentagon? ....

2   Five shapes are drawn below.

   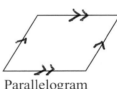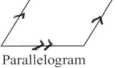   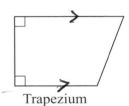

Rectangle   Square   Equilateral   Parallelogram   Trapezium
                               Triangle

State which of the shapes are regular.

....

....

3   Find:

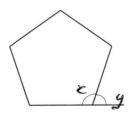

(a) the exterior angle of a regular pentagon.

....

(b) the interior angle of a regular pentagon.

....

Shapes Mini-Exam (1)

1 The shapes below are made up of 1 cm squares.

(a) Find the perimeter and area of these two shapes:

(i)   (ii)

       Perimeter ....   Perimeter ....

       Area ....   Area ....

(b) Is it always true that shapes with larger areas have larger perimeters?
Explain your thinking.

....

....

2 The diagram shows a skateboard ramp in a local park.

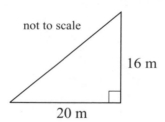

not to scale

16 m

20 m

(a) What is the area of the triangular face? ....

(b) Draw a scale drawing in the space above to find the length of the sloping run.

....

3 The diagram below shows a triangular prism and its incomplete net.

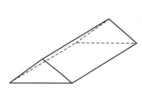   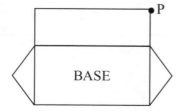

P

BASE

(a) Complete the net of the triangular prism.

(b) Mark any other vertices that will meet at P when the net is folded into the solid.

Shapes Mini-Exam (1)

4 Hal and Leila are using 1 cm cubes to make larger cubes.

(a) Hal is making a cube with sides 3 cm long. How many small cubes will he need?

....

(b) Leila has made a cube using 125 of the small cubes.
     What are the dimensions of the larger cube she has made?

....

5 Match each diagram with the right card. You may use a mirror or tracing paper to help you.

(a)

| 1 line of symmetry |
| no rotational symmetry |

(b)

| no lines of symmetry |
| rotational symmetry of order 2 |

(c)

| 3 lines of symmetry |
| rotational symmetry of order 3 |

6 Regular hexagons fit together to fill a space leaving no gaps.

(a) What is the mathematical name for this?

....

a

(b) Calculate the interior angle of a regular hexagon.

....

(c) There are 360° around a point. Explain why hexagons do not leave gaps when fitted together.

....

....

Shapes Mini-Exam (2)

1   The diagram shows a matchbox measuring 5.2 cm by 3.5 cm by 1.4 cm.

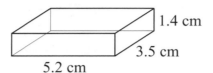

1.4 cm

3.5 cm

5.2 cm

(a) Find the area of the top of the matchbox.

....

(b) Find the total area of all six faces of the matchbox.

....

....

2   Complete the following table. Show all your working.

radius	diameter	circumference	area
	15.8 cm		

....

....

....

3   The length of a cuboid is 15.8 cm. The height of the cuboid is 8.3 cm. Its volume is 1508 cm^3.
What is the width of the cuboid, to 1 decimal place?

....

4   How many cubic centimetres are there in a cubic metre?

....

Shapes Mini-Exam (2)

5 A 50 pence piece is based on a regular heptagon.

(a) Calculate the exterior angle marked *a*, to 2 decimal places.

....

(b) Calculate the interior angle marked *b*, to 2 decimal places.

....

(c) Calculate the sum of all seven interior angles.

....

6 Look at the wedge and the net of the wedge below.

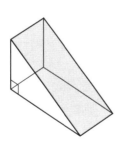 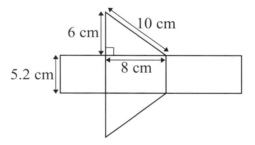

(a) Find the area of the sloping, shaded face.

....

(b) Two of these wedges are fitted together to make a cuboid.

(i) What is the volume of this cuboid?

....

(ii) Hence, what is the volume of the wedge? ....

SECTION THREE — MORE NUMBERS

Metric & Imperial Units

1   Answer these questions on metric conversions:

(a) A car's engine capacity is 1114 cm³. How much is that in litres?

....

(b) A pencil has diameter 1.4 cm. How much is that in mm?

....

(c) The distance John walks to school is 2030 m. How far is that in km?

....

2   Answer these questions on imperial conversions.

(a) Alex's little sister is four feet three inches tall. How many inches is this?

....

(b) A bag of sweets weighs a quarter of a pound. How many ounces is this?

....

(c) Pete's dad buys 3.5 gallons of petrol. How many pints is this?

....

3   Northgate School uses this recipe for pancakes. The measurements are given in metric units.

8 eggs	0.5 kg flour
2 litres milk	pinch salt

(a) Approximately how many pints of milk are needed?

....

(b) Approximately how many pounds of flour are needed?

....

Rounding Off Measurements

1 The table shows the thicknesses of various British coins.
Complete the last column of the table showing the coin thicknesses rounded to the nearest mm.

Coin	Thickness (mm)	Thickness (nearest mm)
1 penny	1.65	2
2 pence	2.03	
50 pence	1.78	
1 pound	3.15	
2 pounds	2.5	

2 Amy has three parcels to send to different relatives for Christmas.
The Parcel Express delivery company has the following charges.

Parcel Express Postage Rates

Weight not over	1 kg	2 kg	3 kg	4 kg
Price	£1.85	£2.45	£3.05	£3.65

(a) Her Grandad's parcel weighs 3.9 kg. How much will it cost Amy to send this parcel?

....

(b) Auntie Maud's parcel weighs 2.1 kg. How much will Amy pay to send this parcel?

....

Amy goes to the Package Pronto delivery company who have a different scale of charges.

Package Pronto Postage Rates

Weight not over	1 kg	1.5 kg	2 kg	2.5 kg	3 kg
Price	£1.50	£2.00	£2.50	£3.00	£3.50

(c) Amy's last parcel weighs 1.8 kg. Which company will it be cheaper to send the parcel with, Parcel Express or Package Pronto?

....

Rounding Off

1. Answer the following questions on rounding off to one or two decimal places.

    (a) Round these numbers off to one decimal place.

        (i)   2.35 ....

        (ii) 8.42 ....

        (iii) 5.96 ....

    (b) Round these numbers off to two decimal places.

        (i)   43.876 ....

        (ii) 6.776 ....

        (iii) 100.489 ....

2. This question involves rounding to the nearest whole number, ten, hundred or thousand.

    (a) At the end of the 2003 season, Liverpool FC had played 3526 premier league matches.
        Round this off to the nearest thousand. ....

    (b) At this time, Liverpool FC had had 883 premiership draws.
        Round this off to the nearest ten. ....

    (c) The average rainfall for Trikkala in Greece in December is 125 mm.
        Round this off to the nearest hundred mm. ....

    (d) The height of Concorde was 12.2 m. Round this off to the nearest metre.

        ....

3. Round these numbers off to one significant figure.

    (a) 576 ....   (c) 17 ....

    (b) 4.9 ....   (d) 99 ....

Estimating & Approximating

1 Estimate the answers to the following:

(a) 51.2×11

....

(b) $62.9 \div 29$

....

(c) $\dfrac{505 \times 2.9}{28.9}$

....

(d) $\dfrac{301}{9.9 \times 2.9}$

....

2 Estimate the answers to these questions.

(a) Colin's bed is 1.98 m long and 1.2 m wide.
Approximately what area of floor space does the bed take up?

....

(b) Rachel's magazine cover measures 21 cm by 29 cm.
Estimate the area of the magazine cover.

....

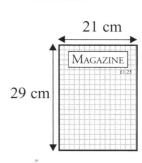

3 The formula for the circumference (distance around the edge) of a circle is $2 \times \pi \times$ radius.
If $\pi = 3.14$, estimate the circumference of a circle with a radius of 5.1 cm.

....

Conversion Graphs

1 This graph converts between pints and litres.

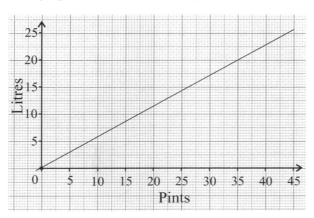

(a) A small farm produces 24 litres of milk every day. How many pints is this?

....

(b) A gallon is 8 pints. How many litres are there in 5 gallons?

....

2 This graph converts between miles per hour (m.p.h.) and kilometres per hour (km/h).

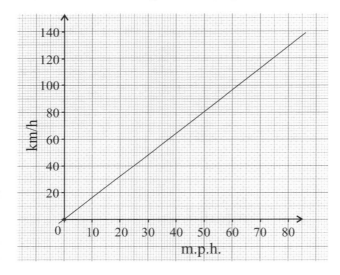

(a) The speed limit on French autoroutes is 110 km/h in wet weather. What is this in m.p.h.?

....

(b) The speed limit in some built-up areas in Britain is 20 m.p.h. What is this in km/h?

....

(c) John's average speed when driving from Birmingham to Manchester is 55 m.p.h.
Pierre's average speed when driving from Paris to Bordeaux is 100 km/h.
Who drives faster on average?

....

Conversion Factors

1.   There are 14 pounds in a stone.

   (a) Mark's little brother Fred weighs 42 pounds. How many stone is that?

   ....

   (b) A box of apples weighs 2 stone. How many pounds is that?

   ....

   (c) Michelle weighs 9.7 stone. Give her weight in pounds?

   ....

2.   Use conversion factors to answer these questions.

   (a) One of the largest dinosaurs was the tyrannosaurus rex.
        The jaw of a tyrannosaurus rex could be about 1.2 metres wide.
        How many centimetres is that?

   ....

   (b) Pete's pet salamander weighs 374 g. Give the salamander's weight in kg.

   ....

3.   £1 buys 10.5 Danish Kroner.

   (a) How much is £22 in Kroner?

   ....

   (b) Convert 30 Kroner to pounds.

   ....

Fractions

1   Answer these questions on fractions.

   (a)   Convert these fractions to decimals.

      (i) $\dfrac{4}{5}$ ....

      (ii) $\dfrac{3}{8}$ ....

      (iii) $2\frac{1}{4}$ ....

      (iv) $7\frac{9}{10}$ ....

   (b)   Cancel these fractions to their simplest terms.

      (i) $\dfrac{9}{18}$ ....

      (ii) $\dfrac{9}{15}$ ....

      (iii) $\dfrac{45}{50}$ ....

      (iv) $\dfrac{22}{121}$ ....

2   Work out the following:

   (a) $\dfrac{2}{5}$ of 195 kg. ....

   (b) $\dfrac{3}{7}$ of 84 miles. ....

   (c) $\dfrac{5}{12}$ of 96 miles. ....

3   Work out these word problems involving fractions.

   (a)   Sam has 15 sweets. He gives $\frac{1}{3}$ of them to Katherine. How many sweets does Katherine get?

      ....

   (b)   Pierre has 40 tins of cat food in his cupboard. He says that in a week his cat will eat $\frac{2}{5}$ of the tins. How many tins does the cat eat in a week?

      ....

   (c)   Jane's mum has £42 in her purse. She gives Jane $\frac{5}{6}$ of this to spend on clothes. How much money does Jane's mum have left?

      ....

Fractions, Decimals & Percentages

1 This question requires you to convert between fractions, decimals and percentages.

(a) Change the following decimals to fractions:

(i) 0.42 .... (ii) 0.7 ....

(iii) 0.07 ....

(b) Change the following fractions to decimals:

(i) $\frac{1}{4}$ .... (ii) $\frac{3}{5}$ ....

(iii) $\frac{2}{3}$ ....

(c) Fill in the missing values in the table.

Fraction	Percentage	Decimal
$\frac{3}{4}$		
	51%	
		0.8

2 Hassan carried out a survey of cars passing the school gates.

(a) 35% of the cars were red. What is this as a fraction?

....

(b) 29% of the cars were blue. Write this as a decimal. ....

(c) 3% were sports cars. Write this as a decimal. ....

3 Convert these quantities into percentages.

(a) One American dollar is worth 0.62 of a British pound. Write this as a percentage.

....

(b) One Euro is approximately $\frac{3}{5}$ of a British pound. What is this as a percentage?

....

Percentages

1   Mark, a builder, charges £1545 plus VAT to build an extension.
    The VAT is charged at 17.5%.
    Work out the total bill.

    ....

    ....

2   Cashin's department store discounts 10% off all prices in the summer sale.
    Work out the sale price of the following items.

(a) A jumper costing £20.

    ....£2..

(b) A frying pan costing £35.

    ....£3.50..

(c) A bottle of perfume costing £18.

    ....£1.80..

3   Peter puts £50 into a building society account.
    The building society pays 4% interest per year.
    How much money does Peter have in the building society after one year?

    ....

    ....

Percentages

1   Jane receives £50 as a birthday present.

   (a)   She spends £7 on make up. What is this as a percentage of £50?

   ....

   ....

   (b)   She spends £21 on clothes. What is this as a percentage of £50?

   ....

   ....

   (c)   She saves the rest of the money. What percentage of the money does she save?

   ....

   ....

2   Clipz stationery shop buys boxes of pencils at 90p each.
   It sells them for £1.10.
   What percentage profit does Clipz make?

   ....

   ....

   ....

3   A car costs £8500 to buy new. After a year the car is worth £7775.
   What is the percentage decrease in the value of the car?

   ....

   ....

More Numbers Mini-Exam (1)

1   Fred has 10 sweets and Mary has 12 sweets.

   (a) Fred eats 8 of his sweets. What percentage of his sweets has he eaten?

   ....

   (b) Mary eats ⅔ of her sweets. How many sweets has she eaten?

   ....

   (c) What fraction of the total number of sweets is left? Give your answer in its simplest form.

   ....

   ....

2   The graph below converts between pounds (£) and Canadian dollars ($).

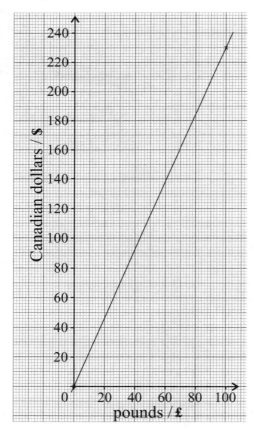

   (a) Pierre is travelling from Montreal in Canada to London. He takes $120 spending money. How much is this in pounds?

   ....

   (b) Nisha takes £80 spending money to Canada. How much is this in Canadian dollars?

   ....

   (c) At the end of their holidays, Nisha has $10 left and Pierre has £9. Who has more money left?

   ....

   ....

   ....

More Numbers Mini-Exam (1)

3   This question is about approximation.

(a)   Mrs. Buckley collects £31.50 in dinner money every week.
Approximately how much money has she collected after 11 weeks? Show your working.

....

(b)   Estimate the value of $\dfrac{3.1+1.85}{1.02\times4.99}$

....

4   Charlie works out some statistics for his school.

(a)   1092 students attend Smallport secondary school. Round this number to 1 significant figure.

....

(b)   The school football pitch is 101.53 m long.

(i)   Round this to the nearest metre. ....

(ii)   What is the precise length of the football pitch in cm? ....

(c)   The average weight of a student at Smallport secondary school is 61.325 kg.

Round this number to 1 decimal place. ....

5   Complete the table below which shows equivalent fractions, decimals and percentages.

Fraction	Percentage	Decimal
$\frac{2}{5}$		
	20%	
		0.08

More Numbers Mini-Exam (2)

1   For this question, you will need to convert between metric and imperial measurements.

   (a)   There are 1.75 pints in a litre. A pack of four cans of cola contains 1.32 litres.
         How many pints is this?

         ....

   (b)   A newborn baby weighs 4 kilograms. How many pounds is this?

         ....

   (c)   The distance between Johannesburg and Cape Town is 789 miles.
         How far is this in kilometres?

         ....

2   Use conversion factors to answer these questions.

   (a) If £1 will buy 1.42 Euros, how many Euros will £3.50 buy?

         ....

   (b) A spider has a head length of 43 mm. Give the length of its head in cm.

         ....

   (c) A jar of Yumeez raspberry jam weighs 454 g. How many kg is this?

         ....

3   A fitter charges £2600 plus VAT for a kitchen. VAT is charged at 17.5%.
     What is the total cost of the kitchen?

         ....

         ....

More Numbers Mini-Exam (2)

4   Peter attempts a sponsored walk of 175 km. He only completes $\frac{2}{7}$ of the walk.
     How far does Peter walk?

     ....

     ....

5   Cancel these fractions to their simplest form.

(a) $\dfrac{35}{49}$ ....

(b) $\dfrac{95}{100}$ ....

(c) $\dfrac{30}{99}$ ....

6   Mr. Smith runs a sweet shop.

(a) Chocco bars cost £3 per box.
     Mr. Smith receives a 10% discount when
     he buys them from the wholesalers.
     How much does Mr. Smith pay per box?

     ....

     ....

(b) On Saturday morning, customers spend a total of £86 in Mr. Smith's sweet shop.
     £14 of this is profit.
     What is his profit as a percentage?

     ....

Mean, Median, Mode & Range

1   Jenny sat twelve mental Maths tests in a term. She scored the following marks out of ten.

4, 7, 3, 1, 4, 6, 8, 4, 5, 7, 5, 6

(a)   Write down the range of marks.

....

(b)   What is the mode of this set of data?

....

(c)   Calculate her mean mark.

....

2   Chris watches the TV weather forecast and writes down the temperature in his city every day for 1 week. Look at his list below. (All values are in °C.)

3, –3, 4, 0, –1, 2, 4.

(a)   What is the mean temperature for these seven days?

....

(b)   What is the median temperature?

....

3   Russell takes four history tests. Each test is out of 20 marks.
He scores 14, 10 and 15 in the first three.
His mean score was 10 for the four tests overall.
What was Russell's mark in the fourth test?

....

....

Tally / Frequency Tables

1 The frequency table below shows the amount of money spent on snacks in one week by one class.

Money spent (£), p	Number of pupils
$0 \leq p < 2$	6
$2 \leq p < 4$	2
$4 \leq p < 6$	10
$6 \leq p < 8$	4

(a)   Draw a bar chart on the axes below to show the data.

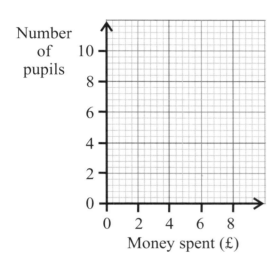

(b)   How many pupils are there in the class?

....

(c)   What is the modal amount of money spent?

....

2 The spinner shown is spun 12 times and the results are recorded below.

3, 0, –2, 1, 1, 3, –2, 3, –2, 1, 0, 1

(a)   Complete the following table to show these results.

Result	Tally	Frequency
–2		
0		
1		
3		

(b)   What is the modal result?   ....

(c)   What is the range of the results?   ....

(d)   What is the median score?   ....

Graphs & Charts

1 The pictogram shows the number of footballs sold by a large sports shop on four Saturdays.

Saturday 1st March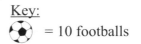

Saturday 8th March ⚽ ⚽

Saturday 15th March ⚽ ⚽ ⚽

Saturday 22nd March ⚽

Key:
⚽ = 10 footballs

(a) How many footballs were sold on 1st March?

....

(b) How many footballs were sold in total on these four Saturdays?

....

2 The table shows the number of pupils staying on at Tickem High School after Year 11.
The school tries to encourage as many pupils as possible in each year to stay on at school.

Year	1999	2000	2001	2002	2003
Pupils	100	85	105	125	110

(a) Draw a frequency polygon to show the data above.

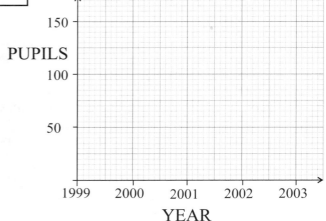

(b) What was the modal year? ....

(c) Jenna says that the school must have done a very bad job of trying to keep pupils in 2000. Is she right? Explain your answer.

....

Graphs & Charts

1 A family of five people decide to plot their heights in metres against their ages in years. Four of the family have plotted their data on the graph below.

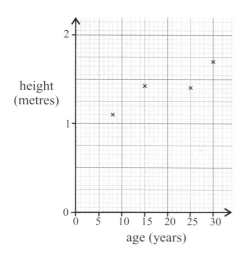

(a) Becky is 8 years old. How tall is she?

....

(b) Norman is 3 years old and 0.8 m tall. Plot Norman's height and age on the graph.

(c) Add a line of best fit to this scatter graph.

(d) Describe the relationship between the family's ages and their heights.

....

....

2 Three pupils take five maths tests, one after the other. Each test is marked out of 10. The scatter graphs below show the three pupils' results.

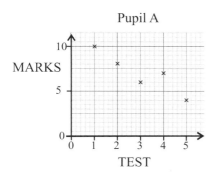
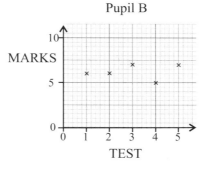
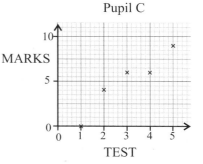

For each pupil describe the relationship between the tests and the marks scored.

(a) Pupil A ....

(b) Pupil B ....

(c) Pupil C ....

Pie Charts

1 Three friends spend part of their leisure time in the evenings reading, watching TV, or using a computer. The pie charts show the proportion of their time that they spend on each activity:

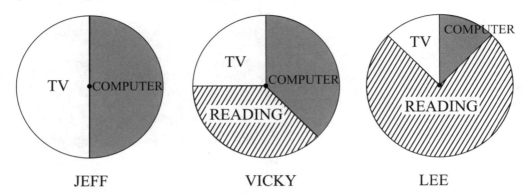

JEFF   VICKY   LEE

(a) Who spends the highest proportion of their time reading? ....

(b) Who spends the smallest proportion of their time reading? ....

(c) Why can we not use the pie charts to say who spends the most time watching TV?

....

2 The table shows the number of hours Leanne spends each day on four activities.

Activity	Time	Angle
lessons	5	
meals	3	
homework	1	
hobbies	3	

(a) Calculate the angles needed to draw a pie chart of this information.

(b) Complete the pie chart below.

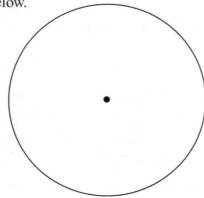

Probability

1 Five friends regularly meet at 7 pm at the cinema to see a film.
The number line shows the percentage probability of each friend arriving on time.

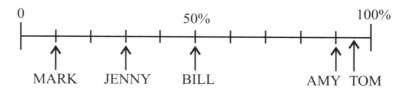

(a) What is the probability of Jenny arriving on time? ....

(b) Who is least likely to arrive on time? ....

(c) Who is as likely to arrive late as on time? ....

2 There are six numbers on a normal die.
The die is rolled.

(a) What is the probability of rolling a six? ....

(b) What is the probability of rolling a three? ....

(c) What is the probability of rolling a two or a three?

....

3 The probability line below shows the probability of it being cloudy on any given day in a
month. There is a 50% chance of an April day being cloudy.

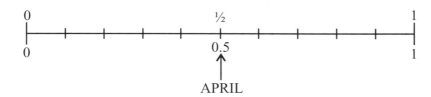

(a) The probability of a June day being cloudy is ¼. Mark June on the probability line.

(b) The probability of a November day being cloudy is 0.7. Mark November on the line.

(c) There is a 60% chance of a January day being cloudy. Mark January on the line.

Probability

1 A box contains three types of solid: cubes, spheres and pyramids.
Each solid is either black, grey or white as shown below.

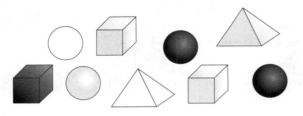

Kylie picks out a solid at random.

(a) What is the probability that she takes out a grey solid?

....

(b) What is the probability that she takes out a cube?

....

(c) What is the probability of her taking out a solid which is either white or grey?

....

(d) What is the probability of Kylie removing a black pyramid?

....

2 A bag contains 20 sweets, all of which are either lemon, lime or strawberry flavoured.
6 of them are lemon flavoured. The probability of picking a strawberry flavoured one is $\frac{2}{5}$.

(a) What is the probability of picking a lemon flavoured sweet at random?

....

(b) How many strawberry flavoured sweets are there in the bag?

....

(c) What is the probability of picking a lime sweet at random?

....

(d) What is the probability of choosing a sweet which is not lime flavoured?

....

First Quadrant Coordinates

1 A group of pupils are writing their initials on grids.

(a) Louise has joined three points on the grid to make her initial.

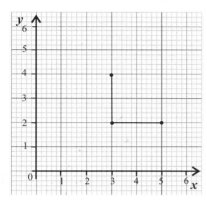

Write down the coordinates of the points she used.

(3 , 4)

(3 , 2)

(5 , 2)

(b) Vinnie starts to write his initial.

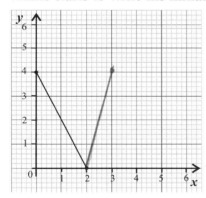

(i) Add another point to make Vinnie's initial.

(ii) Write down the coordinates of the three points.

(2 , 0)

(0 , 4)

(3 , 4)

(c) Another pupil uses these coordinates to write her initial.

(4, 2)   (4, 5)   (5, 4)   (6, 5)   (6, 2)

(i) Plot these points on the grid and join them up in order with straight lines.

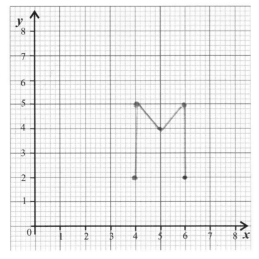

(ii) Which letter have you drawn?

.... M ....

Positive & Negative Coordinates

1 Points A, B and C are plotted on the axes below.

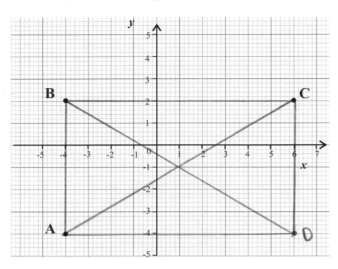

(a) Write down the coordinates of points A, B and C.

A (-4 , -4)

B (-4 , 2)

C (6 , 2)

(b) Plot the point D on the grid so that ABCD is a rectangle.

(c) Draw the diagonals of the rectangle.
Write down the coordinates of the point where the diagonals cross.

.... 1,−1 ....

2 Here is a set of axes on a grid:

(a) On the grid, plot the points: P (–2, 3)   Q (3, 3)   R (3, 0)   S (–2, –3)

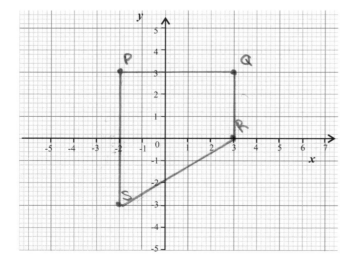

(b) What is the mathematical name of the shape PQRS? ....

(c) What are the equations of the lines PQ and PS?

PQ ....   PS ....

Common Graphs

1   Answer the following questions using the grid below.

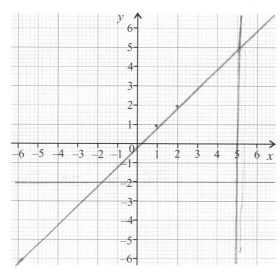

(a) On the grid draw the following lines:

  (i) $x = 5$

  (ii) $y = -2$

  (iii) $y = x$

(b) Write down the coordinates of the point where the lines $x = 5$ and $y = x$ meet.

  5,5

(c) What sort of triangle have the three lines made?

  right angled triangle

2   There are three lines drawn on the axes below.

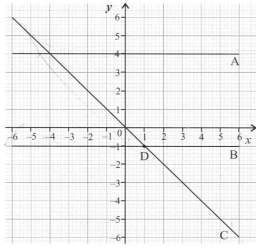

(a) Write down the equation of the line labelled A.

(b) Write down the equation of the line labelled B.

(c) Write down the equation of the line labelled C.

(d) Write down the coordinates of the point labelled D.

(e) Circle the word or words below which describe the lines A and B.

   skew   perpendicular   parallel

Drawing Graphs from Equations

1 There are some values missing in the table below.

x	−3	−2	−1	0	1	2	3
y					5		

(a) Complete the table of values using the equation $y = 2x + 3$.

(b) Use the table of values to plot the graph of $y = 2x + 3$ on the grid below.

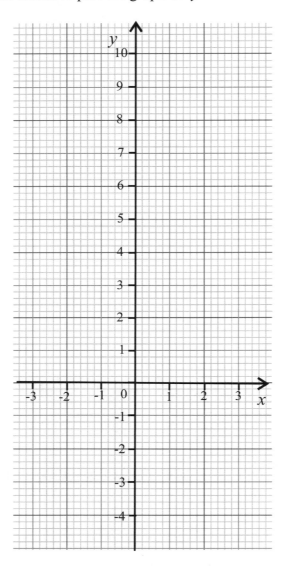

(c) On the same grid draw the line $y = 2$.

(d) Write down the coordinates of the point where these two lines meet.

....

Drawing Graphs from Equations

1 There are some values missing in the table below.

x	−3	−2	−1	0	1	2	3
y			3			6	

(a) Complete the table of values shown above using the equation $y = x^2 + 2$

(b) Use the table of values to plot the graph of $y = x^2 + 2$ on the grid below.

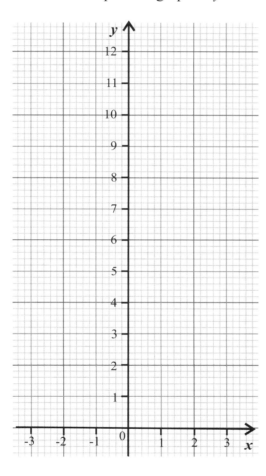

(c) From your graph, find the value of y when $x = 2.4$. Give your answer to 1 decimal place.

....

(d) Substitute $x = 2.4$ into $y = x^2 + 2$ to find the exact value of y when $x = 2.4$.

....

Statistics & Graphs Mini-Exam (1)

1 The marks gained by 30 pupils in one of their SATs exams are given below:

19 32 35 48 39 50 32 26   8 27 22 34 25 22 17
45 34 11 49 32 29 38 44 37 20 56 38 15 41 31

(a) Complete the frequency table.

Marks, m	Tally	Frequency, f
$0 \leq m < 10$		
$10 \leq m < 20$		
$20 \leq m < 30$		
$30 \leq m < 40$		
$40 \leq m < 50$		
$50 \leq m < 60$		

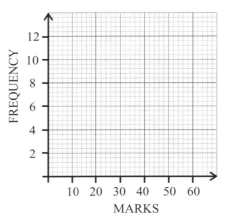

(b) Use the axes above to draw a bar chart representing the information in the frequency table.

(c) One pupil is chosen at random. What is the probability that they scored less than 20 marks?

....

2 The graphs below show how the sales from a school tuck shop vary with the daily temperature.

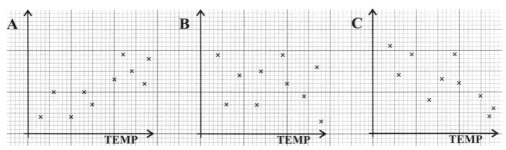

The horizontal axis on each graph is labelled temperature.

(a) Below are the labels for the vertical axes.
Write the letter of the appropriate graph next to each label.

(i) sales of hot chocolate ....

(ii) sales of ice-pops ....

(iii) sales of crisps ....

(b) Describe the correlation in diagram C.

....

Statistics & Graphs Mini-Exam (1)

3 The school tuck shop has a choice of fruit drinks and flavours of crisps.
Below is a list of the drinks and crisps available.

Fruit Drinks	Crisps
orange	chicken
apple	bacon
lemon	ready salted
mango	

Katy buys one drink and one packet of crisps at random.

(a) Write a list of all the possible combinations of drink and crisps that Katy could have.

....

....

....

....

(b) What is the probability that Katy chooses a mango drink and a packet of bacon crisps?

....

(c) What is the probability that Katy chooses an apple drink with any flavour of crisps?

....

4 A, B and C are points on the grid below.

(a) Write down the coordinates of point B.

....

ABCD is a rhombus.

(b) Mark and label the point D on the grid.

(c) Write down the equation of the line BC.

....

(d) (i) On the grid, draw a line through D parallel to the x-axis.

(ii) What is the equation of the line you have drawn?

....

Statistics & Graphs Mini-Exam (2)

1 Joe can catch either bus A or bus B to get to the football match.
The waiting times for bus A on the last 8 journeys were as follows:

3 mins	3 mins	6 mins	4 mins
6 mins	5 mins	6 mins	7 mins

(a) Calculate the mode, median, mean and range of these times.

....

....

For bus B, the data for the last 8 journeys is as follows:

mode = 3 mins   median = 3 mins
mean = 4·5 mins   range = 11 mins

(b) Which bus would be the better one for Joe to catch?
You must explain your answer using the data from above.

....

....

2 A box of jellybeans contains the following numbers of different coloured beans.

Colour of jellybean	Number
yellow	23
red	34
green	18
white	15
purple	30

(a) Using the space below, display this data in a pie chart and label it clearly.

(b) Which colour jellybean has a probability of ¼ of being chosen at random from the box?

....

(c) What is the probability that the jellybean chosen is not white?

....

Statistics & Graphs Mini-Exam (2)

 Class 8A and Class 8B conducted experiments to see if a spinner numbered 1 to 4 was biased.

3

(a) Class 8A spun the spinner 50 times and recorded the numbers it landed on.
Their results are given below:

Number on spinner	Number of times	Probability
1	12	
2	8	
3	13	
4	17	

Calculate the probability of the spinner landing on each of the numbers.
Write in the table and give your answers as decimals.

(b) Class 8B spun the spinner 200 times and recorded the numbers it landed on.
Their results are given below:

Number on spinner	Number of times	Probability
1	42	
2	44	
3	36	
4	78	

Calculate the probability of the spinner landing on each of the numbers.
Write in the table and give your answers as decimals.

(c) Using these probabilities decide if the spinner is biased. Explain your answer.

....

....

(d) Which results give better estimates of the probabilities? Explain your answer.

....

(e) If the spinner was spun 1000 times, approximately how many times would you expect it to land on number 4?

....

Clocks & Calendars

1 Here is a calendar for October and November.

OCTOBER

MON	TUES	WED	THURS	FRI	SAT	SUN
		1	2	3	4	5
6	7	8	9	10	11	12
13	14	15	16	17	18	19
20	21	22	23	24	25	26
27	28	29	30	31		

NOVEMBER

MON	TUES	WED	THURS	FRI	SAT	SUN
					1	2
3	4	5	6	7	8	9
10	11	12	13	14	15	16
17	18	19	20	21	22	23
24	25	26	27	28	29	30

(a) What day is the 12th October?

....

(b) (i) A school half-term holiday starts on the last Monday of October.
On what date does the holiday begin?

....

(ii) The holiday lasts one week. On what date does the school term start again?

....

2 A television programme starts at 7:30 pm and lasts 1 hour and 50 minutes.

(a) What time does the programme finish?

....

(b) The programme is recorded on a 3-hour video tape.
How much time is left on the video tape?

....

3 A bus journey starts at 16:20 and ends at 18:05.

(a) Write the start and end times in the 12 hour clock.

....

(b) How long does the bus journey last?

....

Compass Directions & Bearings

1 This map shows some towns in Cumbria.

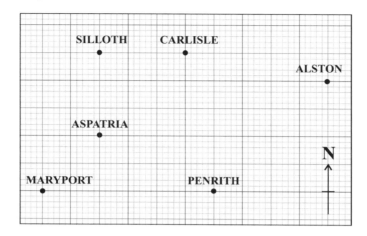

(a) Which town is north of Aspatria?

....

(b) What direction is Maryport from Penrith?

....

(c) Alston is north-east from which town?

....

2 The diagram shows the path of a bird as it flies from tree A to tree B.

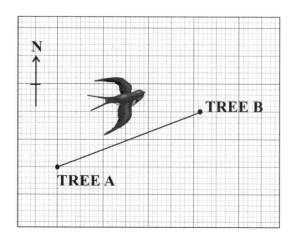

(a) What is the bearing of tree B from tree A?

....

(b) The bird then flies from tree B on a bearing of 135 degrees. Draw a line to show the direction that the bird flies.

Maps & Scales

1   The map shows Mystery Island. The scale is 1 cm : 2 km.

(a) (i) Measure the distance from the Banyan Tree to the Castle on the map.

....

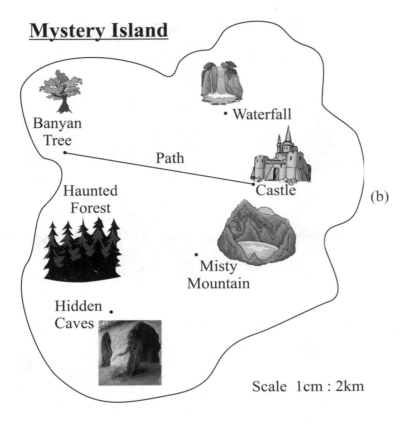

Mystery Island

Scale 1cm : 2km

(ii) Work out the distance from the Banyan Tree to the Castle on the island.

....

....

(b) (i) Measure the distance from the Misty Mountain to the Hidden Caves on the map.

....

(ii) Work out the distance from the Misty Mountain to the Hidden Caves on the island.

....

....

(c) Treasure is buried on the path between the Banyan Tree and the Castle.
The treasure is 1.5 km from the Castle. Mark the position of the treasure on the map.

2   This model car is made to a scale of 1:50 cm

(a) How long is the car in real life?

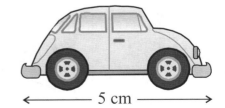

....

(b) A bus is 8 m long.

How long would a model of it be if it was made to the same scale as the car?

....

Lines & Angles

1 Put angles A, B, C, D, and E in order of size, smallest first.

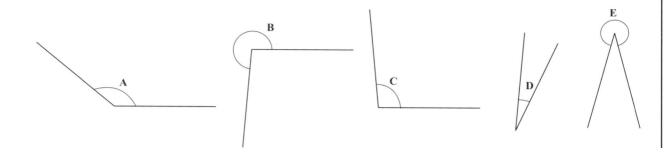

....

2 Match each angle to the correct letter:

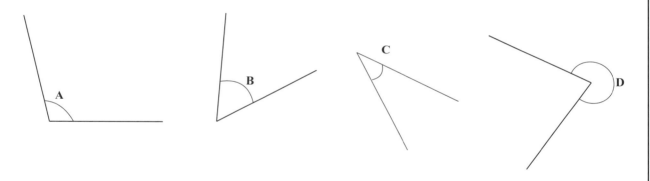

37° = ...   280° = ...   57° = ...   103° = ...

3 Estimate the size of these angles.

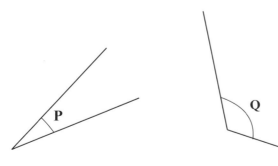

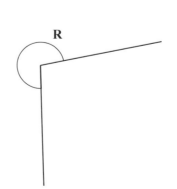

P = ...   Q = ...   R = ...

Measuring Angles

1 Look at these angles.

(a) (i) What is the name of this type of angle?

....

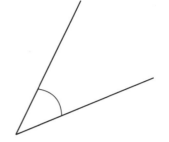

(ii) Measure the angle.

....

(b) (i) What is the name of this type of angle?

....

(ii) Measure the angle.

....

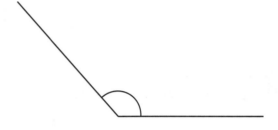

2 Measure the angles in this triangle.

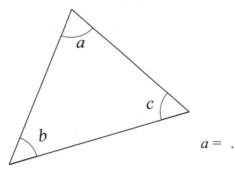

$a = $ .... $b = $ .... $c = $ ....

3 Use a protractor to draw these angles.

(a)   (b)

35°   145°

Angle Rules

1   Calculate the size of each of these angles. The shapes are not drawn to scale.

(a)

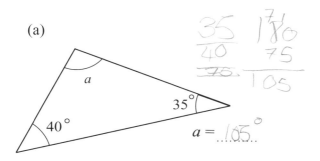

$$\begin{array}{cc} 35 & \overset{71}{180} \\ \underline{40} & \underline{75} \\ \cancel{75} & 105 \end{array}$$

$a = \underline{105}°$

(b)

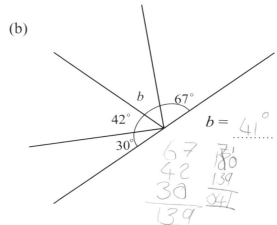

$b = \underline{41}°$

$$\begin{array}{cc} 67 & \overset{71}{180} \\ 42 & \underline{139} \\ \underline{30} & \overset{}{041} \\ 139 & \end{array}$$

(c)

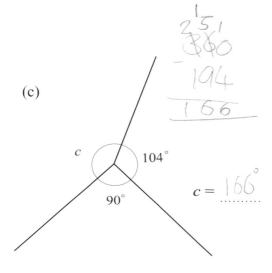

$$\begin{array}{c} \overset{1\ 51}{360} \\ -104 \\ \hline 166 \end{array}$$

$c = \underline{166}°$

(d)

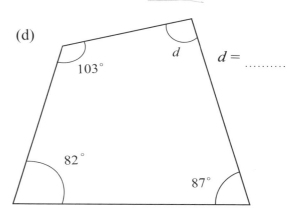

$d = \underline{}$

2   Calculate the size of each of these angles. The shapes are not drawn to scale.

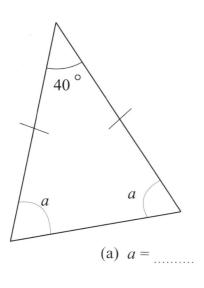

(a) $a = \underline{}$

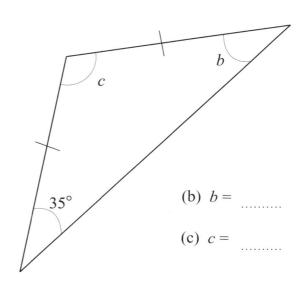

(b) $b = \underline{}$

(c) $c = \underline{}$

Angle Notation

1 Write down the size of these angles.

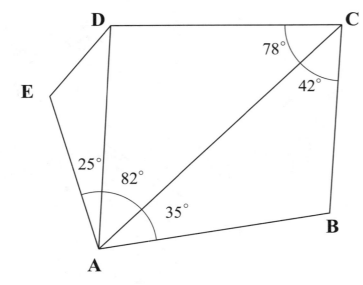

(a) angle ACB

....

(b) angle BAC

....

(c) angle DCA

....

(d) angle EAD

....

2 Calculate the size of these angles.

(a) RQS

....

(b) PRQ

....

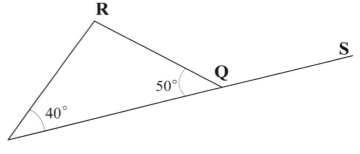

3 You will need to use a protractor for this question.

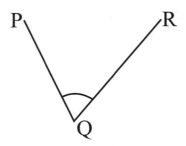

A ——————— B

(a) Measure angle PQR.

(b) Draw angle BAC so that it measures 115°.

....

Congruence

1 Write down the shapes that are congruent to shape A.

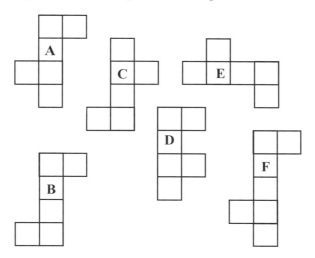

....

2 Shapes P, Q and R are congruent.

Draw two more shapes that are congruent to shapes P, Q and R.

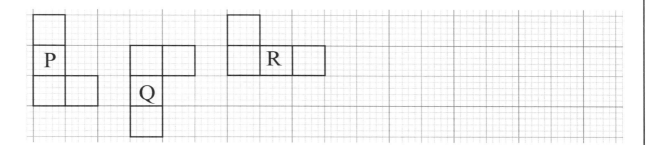

3 Shape AED is a triangle.

(a) Which other triangle in the diagram is congruent to AED?

....

(b) Write down the name of a triangle in the diagram which is congruent to BDC.

....

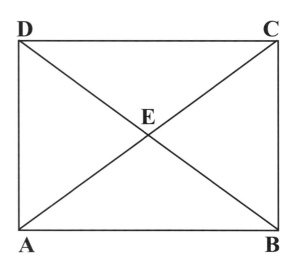

Rotation

1 The shaded rectangle is rotated as shown so that point A stays in the same place.
Mark on the diagram the new position of point B.

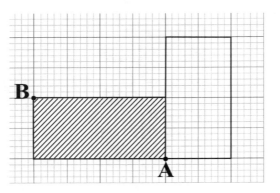

2 Shape A can be rotated clockwise onto shape B.

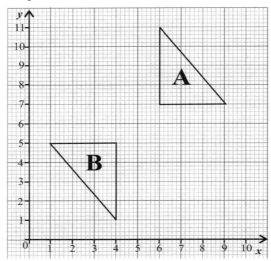

(a) Draw a cross to show the centre of rotation.

(b) What is the angle of rotation?

....

3 Draw this shape rotated 180° clockwise
about the origin. You may use tracing
paper to help you.

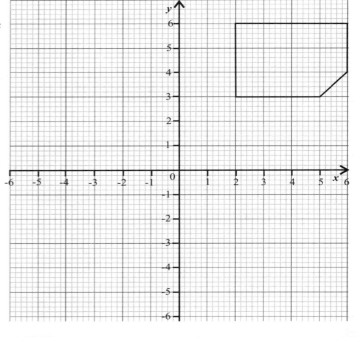

Reflection

1 Reflect these shapes in the mirror lines.
You may use a mirror or tracing paper to help you.

(a)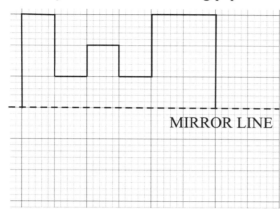

(b)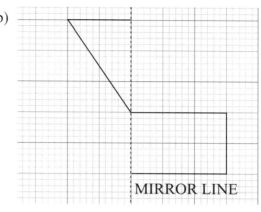

2 These diagrams show shapes that have been reflected in a mirror line.
Draw in the mirror lines. You may use a mirror or tracing paper to help you.

(a)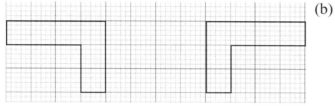

(b)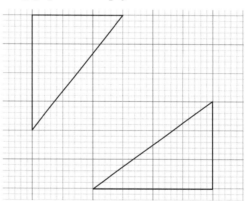

3 Draw a reflection of the shape in the line $y = x$.
You may use a mirror or tracing paper to help you.

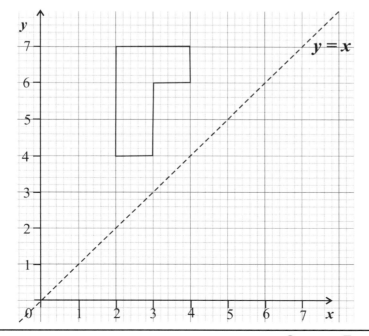

Angles & Other Bits Mini-Exam (1)

1   A 1 week holiday begins on Saturday 29th May and ends on the following Saturday.
    On what date does the holiday end?

    ....

2   The graph below shows 9 shapes labelled A to I.

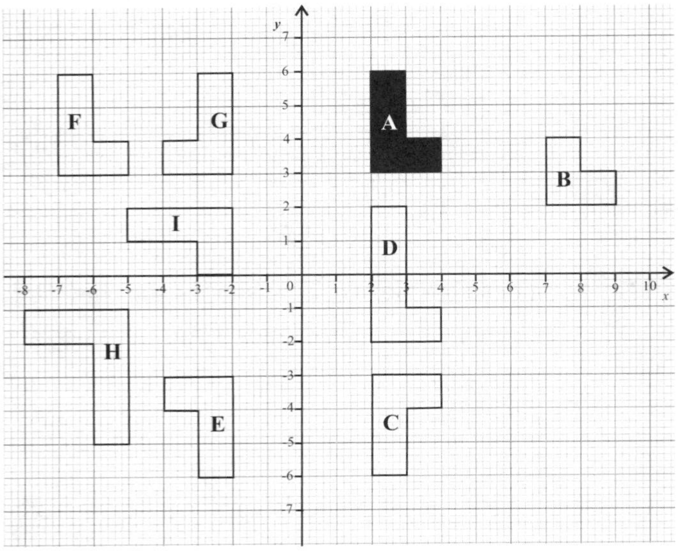

    (a)   Write down the shape that is:

          (i)   A reflection of **A** in the *y*-axis.

                ....

          (ii) A reflection of **A** in the *x*-axis.

                ....

          (iii) A rotation of **A** 180° clockwise
                about the origin.

                ....

    (b)   Which shapes are congruent to shape **A**?

          ....

3   A plan of a house is drawn to a scale of 1:100.

    (a)   A wall on the plan is 4.5 cm. How long is the actual wall?

          ....

    (b)   A fence is 11 m long. How long is the fence on the plan?

          ....

4   What is the definition of a regular polygon?

    ....

    ....

    ....

Angles & Other Bits Mini-Exam (1)

5 Work out the size of:

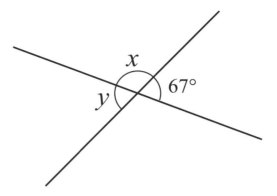

(a) angle x

....

(b) angle y

....

6 Look at the angles a and b shown below.

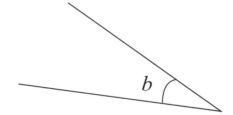

(a) What type of angle is angle:

(i) a? ....

(ii) b? ....

(b) Estimate the size of these angles.

(i) angle a = ...

(ii) angle b = ...

7 Shapes A and B are golf flags. You may use a mirror or tracing paper to help you with this question.

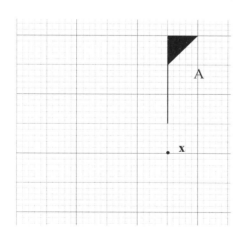
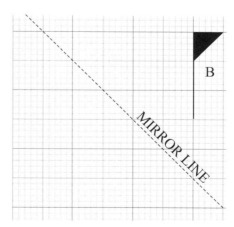

(a) Rotate shape A 90° anti-clockwise about centre of rotation X.

(b) Reflect shape B in the mirror line.

Angles & Other Bits Mini-Exam (1)

8 This is part of a bus timetable.

Acacia Avenue	12:46	13:01	13:16	13:31
English Street	12:58	13:13	13:28	13:43
Market Square	13:03	13:18	13:33	13:48
Railway Station	13:13	13:28	13:43	13:58
Bus Station	13:17	13:32	13:47	14:02

(a) A bus leaves Acacia Avenue at 13:16.

Write this time in the 12 hour clock.

....

(b) How long does it take for the bus to go from English Street to the Bus Station?

....

(c) If you arrive at the Market Square at 1:20 pm, how long do you have to wait for the next bus?

....

9 A robot can move from A to B by moving 3 steps north and 2 steps east.

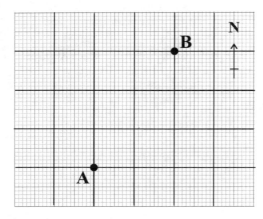

Give instructions for the robot to move from B to A.

....

....

Angles & Other Bits Mini-Exam (2)

1   A map is drawn to a scale of 1 cm to 5 km. Two villages are 12 km apart.
    How far apart are the villages on the map?

    ....

    ....

2   RST is an isosceles triangle. Angle RTS = 47°.

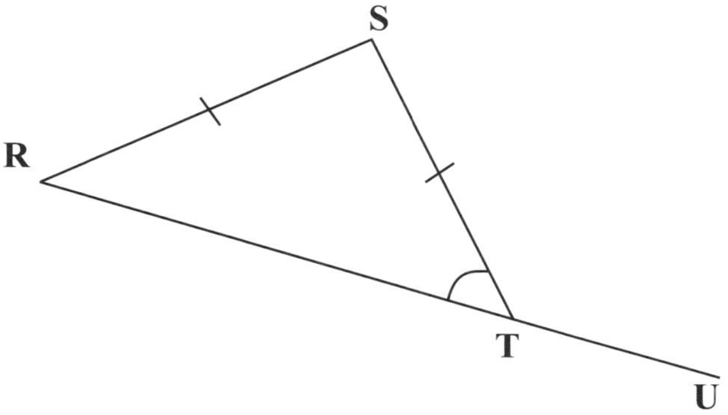

    Work out the size of:

    (a)   Angle SRT

    ....

    (b)   Angle RST

    ....

    (c)   Angle STU

    ....

3   Beeston is south of Aylesbury and Carlton is exactly south-east of Beeston. The distance
    between Beeston and Aylesbury is the same as the distance between Beeston and Carlton.

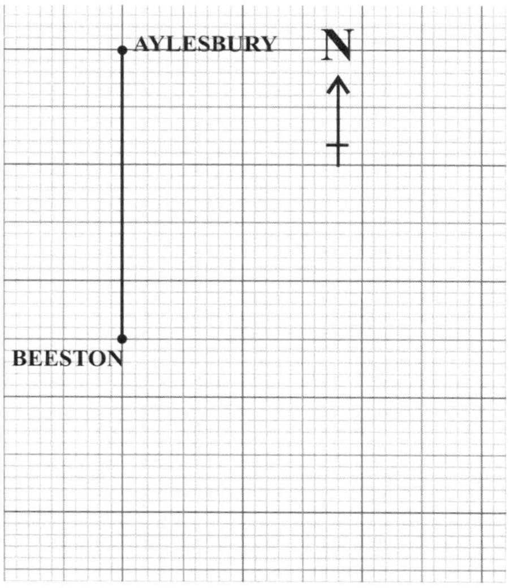

    (a)   Mark the position of Carlton on the diagram.

    (b)   Work out the bearing of Carlton from Beeston.

    ....

SECTION SIX — ALGEBRA

Balancing

1 A grocer weighed some fruit and vegetables on a set of scales and noticed that three bananas balanced with two apples and that four carrots balanced with two bananas.

How many carrots would he need to balance with one apple?

....

....

2 Look at these two sets of scales.

The white balls are twice as heavy as the grey balls, and the black balls are twice as heavy as the white balls.

(a) How many grey balls are needed to balance with one white and one black ball?

....

....

(b) How many white balls are needed to balance with two grey and three black balls?

....

....

Powers

1 What is another name for the mathematical word 'powers'?

....

2  For each of the following statements, say whether they are true or false.

(a) $2^3 = 3^2$ .... False ....

(b) $4^2 = 2^4$ .... True ....

(c) $6^1 = 6$ .... True ....

(d) $3^5 = 15$ .... False ....

3 What is five cubed minus one squared?

.... 124 ....

4 What is six to the power of five?

.... 7776 ....

5 Given that $2^7 = 128$, what is 2^6 equal to?

.... 64 ....

6 Evaluate $1.2^3 - 0.4^2$

....

7 If $1^x \times x^4 = 16$, what is x?

.... 2 ....

Square Roots

1 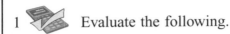 Evaluate the following.

    (a) $\sqrt{144}$ ...... 12 ....

    (b) $\sqrt{256}$ .... 16 ....

15   1 6

2 6 5
3 6 5
  3 2 5
3 9 0 0
    (c) $\sqrt{42.25}$ ...... 6.5 ....
4 2.2 5

2  What is the square root of 81?

        9
....

1 82
8 2
1 1 6 4
1 7 6 0
1 9 2 4

3  Give one reason why the square root of 7056 cannot be equal to 82.

    because   82 x 82 = 6724 ....

4 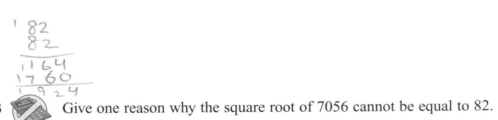 If $\sqrt{x} = 14$, what is x?

    196 ....

5 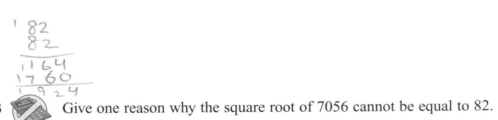 If $\sqrt{6.76} = 2.6$, what is $\sqrt{676}$?

      26 ....

Number Patterns & Sequences

1   Fill in the missing numbers in the following sequences:

(a) 5   7   9   11   ....

(c) 18 15   9   3

(b) 2   10   14   22

(d) 243   9   3   1

2   Here are the first three patterns in a series of picture patterns:

1   •   2   • •   3   • • •
    •   • •   • • •
 • • •   • • • •   • • • • •

(a) Sketch what pattern number 4 should look like.

(b) How many dots will there be in pattern number 6? ....

3   The first three terms of a number sequence are 1, 2, 4.

(a) (i) Suggest a way of continuing the sequence by filling in the next three terms.

     1 2 4   ....

     (ii) What is the rule for this sequence? ....

(b) (i) Suggest another way of continuing the sequence by filling in the next three terms.

     They must be different from those in part (a).

     1 2 4   ....

     (ii) What is the rule for this new sequence? ....

4   What are the next two terms in each of the following sequences?

(a) 11 3 12 6 13 9 14 12   ....

(b) 4 6 5 7 6 8 7   ....

(c) 1 3 4 12 13 39   ....

Number Pattern Formulas

1 Find the nth number in these sequences:

(a) 0, 5, 10, 15, 20, ...

(b) 1, 5, 9, 13, 17, ...

(c) −10, −7, −4, −1, 2, ...

(d) 9, 6, 3, 0, −3, ...

2 For each of the following sequences, give the next two numbers and then state the rule.

(a) 2, 4, 6, 8, ...

(b) 2, 4, 8, 16, ...

(c) 600, 60, 6, 0.6, ...

(d) $1, \frac{1}{2}, \frac{1}{4}, \frac{1}{8},$ ....

3 The first four terms of a sequence are shown below
6, 10, 14, 18, ...

(a) What will the next two terms be? ....

(b) Find an expression for the nth term. ....

(c) The last number in the sequence is 102. How many terms are there? ....

....

4 A chain is made up of a number of similar links.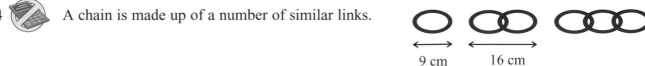

9 cm   16 cm

The length of a single link is 9 cm and the length of two links interlocked is 16 cm.

(a) How long would a chain of 3 links be? ....

(b) How long is a chain consisting of n links? ....

Negative Numbers

1   Put the following numbers in order of size, smallest first.

    2, −1, −5, 7, 3, −4, −6 ....

2   The Christmas Day temperatures in certain cities were recorded and listed in the table below:

City	Temp °C
Amsterdam	−1
Madrid	6
Montreal	−7
New York	−3
Paris	4
Venice	2

(a)   Which city was the coldest?

    ....

(b)   What was the difference in the temperature between Paris and Montreal?

    ....

(c)   In the evening, the temperature in New York fell by 12°C, what was the new temperature?

    ....

(d)   On New Year's Day, the temperature in Venice was −4°C.

    By how much had the temperature fallen since Christmas Day?

    ....

(e)   Christmas Day was the coldest temperature recorded in Amsterdam in December.
The highest temperature was 9°C.
What was the temperature range for Amsterdam in December?

    ....

Negative Numbers

1 Work out the following

(a) –5 + –3 ....

(b) 6 × –2 ....

(c) 15 – (–8) ....

(d) –2 × –4 ....

(e) 15 ÷ –3 ....

(f) –10 ÷ –5 ....

2 Evaluate $\dfrac{-258 + 366}{12}$

....

3 Fill in the boxes using the signs +, –, ×, or ÷. It may be appropriate to leave some boxes blank.

–2 ☐ –6 = ☐ 8

5 ☐ –3 = ☐ 8

6 ☐ –3 = ☐ 2

–4 ☐ –2 = ☐ 8

–4 ☐ 6 = ☐ 2

SECTION SIX — ALGEBRA

a quiz show, Bob got 6 points for correct answers but lost 3 points for
irt. In the second round he lost another 5 points for cheating, but got 8
vers. How many points did he end up with?

....

Basic Algebra

1 Simplify the following expressions:

   (a) $5x - 4 + 2x + 2 - x$

   (b) $c^2 - c + 3c^2 - 2c$

   (c) $x^2 - y^2 + 3x^2 - y^2$

   (d) $x^2 + xy + y^2 - 2xy - x^2$

2  Multiply out the brackets.

   (a) $6(x + 2)$

   (b) $3(a - 1)$

   (c) $p(2p + 3q - r)$

   (d) $2f(g^2 - 3h)$

3 Multiply out the brackets, then simplify the following expressions.
   E.g. $2(a - b) + 3(a + b) = 2a - 2b + 3a + 3b = 5a + b$

   (a) $2q(4p - 3) + 3q(2 - p)$

   (b) $3(2s + t) + 2(s + 2t)$

   (c) $2m(2m - 3) + m(m - 3)$

4 The cost of a video recorder is $(2x - 3)$ pounds and the cost of a television is twice the price.
   Find in terms of x:

   (a) the cost of the television.

   (b) the cost of buying both a television and a video recorder.

Temperature Formulas

1 The formula for converting degrees Celsius into degrees Fahrenheit is:

$$F = \frac{9C}{5} + 32$$

Use this formula to convert the following into °F.

(a) 20°C

....

(b) 50°C

....

(c) 85°C

....

2 Freezing point is 0°C. Write down what this is in degrees Fahrenheit.

....

3 The formula for converting degrees Fahrenheit into degrees Celsius is:

$$C = \frac{5}{9} \times (F - 32)$$

Use this formula to convert the following into °C.

(a) 50°F

....

(b) 113°F

....

(c) 212°F

....

Making Formulas from Words

1   If I take a number N, divide it by three and then subtract four, I get P.
Write down a formula for P in terms of N.

....

2   To find Y, square X, multiply by four and add three. Write down a formula for Y in terms of X.

....

3   A gardener charges £x per hour and works for h hours a day for five days a week.
What is her weekly wage in terms of x and h?

....

4   Helen runs some stables.
To buy a name-plate for a stable door costs £20 for the plate and £1 for every letter in the
horse's name. Write down a formula for the cost C (in pounds) for a name-plate with n letters
on it.

....

5   A will stated that £5000 of an estate E should be left to charity, with the remainder being
divided equally between three sons. Form an equation that gives the inheritance I, in terms of
E, that each of the sons receives (in pounds).

....

Trial and Improvement

For these questions, you may need to use some scrap paper.

1 Solve the following equations using trial and improvement.

(a) $2x + 5 = 4x - 1$ ....

(b) $16 - y = 6y - 5$ ....

(c) $10 - 2x = 3x$ ....

2 Amy and Jim were both given the equation $30 + 11x = 15x - 18$ to solve.
Amy said the value of x was between 1 and 5 whilst Jim said that x was between 11 and 15.

(a) Who was correct? ....

(b) What is the exact solution? ....

3 If $x^2 = 29$ find, using trial and improvement, the value of x correct to 1 decimal place.
You must show all your working.

....

....

4 The volume of a sphere is given by the formula $V = \frac{4}{3}\pi r^3$.

The volume of a ball is 120 cm³. Use trial and improvement to find the radius r to 1 d.p.
Take π to be equal to 3.14 and show all your working.

....

....

5 Solve this equation for x: $\frac{x}{4} = \frac{9}{x}$

....

....

Algebra Mini-Exam (1)

1   When weighing some wooden letters, two Is were found to balance with an O and two Os balanced with a B.

How many Is would be required to balance with a B and an O together?

....

2   Look at this list of numbers:
   2, −5, 7, −4, −1, 3

   (a) Arrange the numbers in order of size, smallest first. ....

   (b) What is the range of the numbers? ....

   (c) Work out the sum of the numbers (i.e. add them all together). ....

3   Danny is twice as old as Richard was 5 years ago. Richard is now r years old.

   (a) Write an expression in terms of r for Richard's age 5 years ago. ....

   (b) Hence write down what Danny's age is now, in terms of r. ....

   The sum of their ages now is 29 years.

   (c) Use this information to form an equation in r. ....

   (d) By trial and improvement, or otherwise, solve the equation to find Richard's age.

   ....

   ....

4   Here is the start of a number sequence:
   3, 7, 11, 15, 19...

   (a) Find the nth term for this sequence. ....

   (b) What is the 25th term for this sequence? ....

Algebra Mini-Exam (1)

5 Simplify the following:

(a) $2w - 3x + 5x - w$

(b) $4y + 7 - 3 + y$

Expand the brackets by multiplying out and simplify:

(c) $4a(b - c) + 2a(c - 2b)$

(d) $p(p + q) + 2p(p - q)$

6 Work out the following:

(a) $\sqrt{64}$

(b) 2^3

(c) $5^1 + 6^2$

7 The diagram shows the first three patterns in a series made with black and white sticks.

Pattern 1   Pattern 2   Pattern 3

(a) Sketch what pattern 4 should look like.

(b) How many white sticks will be in the nth pattern?

(c) How many black sticks will be in the nth pattern?

(d) How many sticks in total will be in pattern 10?

8 The length of a rectangle is 5 cm longer than its width. If its width is $3x$ cm:

(a) write down an expression in x for its length.

(b) what is the perimeter (distance all the way round) of the rectangle, in terms of x.
Write your answer in its simplest form.

Algebra Mini-Exam (2)

1      Calculate:

   (a) 4^5 ....   (b) $\sqrt{1681}$ ....

   (c)   The square root of 3^6 ....

   (d)   Fourteen squared ....

2   To convert degrees Celsius (*C*) to degrees Fahrenheit (*F*) multiply *C* by nine, divide the answer by five and then add 32 to give you *F*.

   (a)   Write down the formula for finding *F* in terms of *C*. ....

   (b)   Use the formula to convert the following into °F:

      (i)   5°C ....

      (ii)   90°C ....

      (iii) 35°C ....

3   Work out:

   (a) $-111 + 48 + 203 - 87 - (-5)$ ....   (b) 8×-32 ....

   (c) $-93 \div -3$ ....   (d) -9×-13 ....

4   If $x^4 = 29$, use trial and improvement to find *x* correct to 1 decimal place. Remember to show all your working. The first two trials have been done for you.

x	x^4	
2	16	too small
3	81	too big

   ....

   ....

   ....

Algebra Mini-Exam (2)

5 The first five terms of a sequence are:

4, 8, 16, 32, 64, ...

(a) State the rule for finding the next number in the sequence.

....

This is a sequence of increasing powers of 2:

2^2, 2^3, 2^4, 2^5, $2^6.$...........

(b) What is the nth term of this series? ....

(c) Work out the 17th term. ....

6 Find an exact solution for x using trial and improvement or otherwise.

(a) $\dfrac{48}{x} + x = 14$ ....

....

(b) $\dfrac{100}{x^2} + x = 9$ ....

....

(c) $4 + x + x^2 = 60$ ....

....

7 If $y^2 = 10^2 - 8^2$, what is y?

....

8 Simplify the following:

(a) $3.2x + 0.4 - 0.8x - 0.2$ ....

(b) $4.2 - 3x - 5 + 6.1x$ ....

(c) $-6.4x - 8 + 9.7 + 10x$ ....